Michael F
Chats with Cats

Illustrated
by
Rebecca Hodgkinson

Seven Arches
Publishing

Published in 2023
By Seven Arches Publishing
The Flat, New Inn Farm Beckley, Oxford, OX3 9TY
www.sevenarchespublishing.co.uk

A catalogue record for this book is available from
the British Library.

Cover design and typesetting by Alan McGlynn

Printed in Great Britain

ISBN 978-1-7393302-1-7

When I first started reading Michael Rosen's conversations with his cats, I imagined that his cats were two very special pets – possibly two Siamese. After all, they belonged to one of the most well-known children's author, a poet and a broadcaster who is often on the radio and has a YouTube channel. They must be an expensive breed.

They certainly seemed to think a great deal of themselves, and they didn't seem to be soft and cuddly like a Persian – no they must be lean, sleek and perfectly bred Siamese. But it turned out they were just two ordinary black and white moggies.

Michael Rosen's two cats are called Jack and Meg and if you are not totally enamoured with them by the end of this book you must be…a dog lover.

Michael Rosen has written over 200 books.

Many that are for children feature animals.

There are Bears, Crocodiles, Elephants, Ponies, Hamsters, Rabbits, a farting Fish, even a Fly and, of course, Dogs.

These are the ones with a Cat on the cover:

Rigatoni the Pasta Cat

Dread Cat

I am ANGRY

Don't Forget Tiggs

Blue

For Emma

Me: Have you seen that little tray of sushi?
It was on the table.

Cats: No.

Me: No one else has been in here.

Cats: Not us.

Me: I can't see it anywhere.

Cats: Neither can we.

Me: Oh hang on. It's under the sofa.

Cats: Really?

Me: You put it there, didn't you?

Cats: Probably.

Me: You're sitting on a poem that I have to read on a zoom call in a mo.

Cats: And?

Me: I'm trying to say you should get off it, but I'm being nice about it.

Cats: You're not being nice about it.

Me: Can you please get off it?

Cats: No.

Me: What's the reason now?

Cats: Because.

Cats: You said the white stuff would go away.

Me: I..er...said that it...er...the likelihood...and...er

Cats: You're lying.

Me: I'm not lying, I was just looking at it mathematically.

Cats: There is only one maths.

Me: Really?

Cats: You've only given us one portion this morning.

Cats: We saw a bit of that film you made.

Me: What do you think?

Cats: Not very good.

Me: Oh? Why not?

Cats: We're not in it.

Me: That would be a different film.

Cats: Different and better.

Me: OK what would you do in this film?

Cats: Doze.

Cats: What are you doing?

Me: I'm cutting my nails.

Cats: Stupid.

Me: I have to do it, otherwise they grow long
and break and get dirty.

Cats: Do we cut our nails?

Me: No that's true.

Cats: We wear them down by scratching your sofas.

Cats: There should be an NCS.

Me: Mm?

Cats: National Cat Service.

Me: You get enough service already.
Who got up early to get you your food this morning?

Cats: You want applause for forgetting to buy food yesterday.

Me: Er...no...but...

Cats: Your failings are why we need an NCS.

NCS

National Cat Service

The Safeguarding of
ill-treated cats

Tel:

Visit the
Fish Kitchen
for Tuna Treats
and Warm Milk

12

Cats: This kitchen is a socialist kitchen.

Me: You can't have socialism in one kitchen.

Cats: We worked out it's socialist because
all our food is ours and all your food is ours.

Me: And is all your food mine?

Cats: You don't like our food.

Me: But could it be mine?

Cats: No.

Me: Why are you wet?

Cats: We've been out.

Me: You haven't been peeing on each other?

Cats: Oh for goodness sake.

Me: I'm just checking before I do any stroking.

Cats: Well, forget it. You've ruined the moment.

Me: Didn't take much then, did it?

Cats: We have standards.

Cats: We're in the other room.

Me: I'm in this room.

Cats: We know.
But you didn't know we were in the other room.

Me: I didn't know whether you were or you weren't
in the other room.

Cats: And that's it!
That's what we have to cope with, with you.
Ignorance and indifference.

Me: Why do you hang about behind me
when I'm working?

Cats: To make sure you don't do anything bad.

Me: Like what?

Cats: Not feeding us.

Me: How are you going to stop me doing that?

Cats: Howling all night long till your eyes go red.

Me: You wouldn't.

Cats: Try us.

Cats: We heard you swearing under your breath about how we had lost your post-it notes.

Me: That wasn't me.

Cats: No one else is here.

Me: Well, you've walked off with some other stuff of mine.

Cats: You're not Sherlock Holmes.

Me: You've read Conan Doyle?

Cats: Of course.

Cats: Why are you blaming us
for kicking the cushion off the chair?

Me: Cos you did it.

Cats: As you got up, you pushed the cushion – it fell.

Me: So, you say.

Cats: We're trained to observe. We saw you.

Me: Even if you didn't do it this time,
it's the sort of thing you often do.

Cats: Go out and get us some more food.

Me: There's frost on the ground.

Cats: Why do you always come up with excuses?

Me: You make it sound as if I'm trying to
get out of doing things, as if I make up stuff.

Cats: Yes.

Me: Why do you do that?

Cats: To make you feel guilty.

Cats: We hate each other and we're going to eat each other.

Me: Let's talk about this.

Cats: We despise each other.

Me: That gives us a starting point for our chat.

Cats: How?

Me: You're very alike, with the same feelings,

Cats: Don't interrupt. We're trying to kill each other.

Me: You're walking on my notes.

Cats: So?

Me: They are notes for my next great work of art.

Cats: [smirk]

Me: Yes? Anything you'd like to say?

Cats: As if anything you write is 'great'.

Me: When Emma brought you here,
I had hopes you would appreciate me.

Cats: No chance.

Cats: Where've you been? It's late.

Me: I've been in a school.
It takes a while to get back from Bognor.

Cats: We're starving.

Me: You'll have to wait till I get me coat off, open the
box, tear open the sachets and put it in your bowls.

Cats: Why are you always so complicated?

Me: Can we come to a deal about
you sticking your bums in my face?

Cats: What deal?

Me: Bottom line (if you'll forgive me the gag)
is that I don't like it.

Cats: Our bottom line (when we say it, it's funny)
is that we like it.

Me: But I'm not a cat.

Cats: That's your problem.

Cats: Stop shouting.

Me: Arsenal have scored in the last seconds
to win the game.

Cats: And?

Me: We were two-nil down.

Cats: Down what?

Me: We were losing.

Cats: And?

Me: We won.

Cats: Won what?

Me: The game.

Cats: Just one game?

Me: We won. We won. We won.

Cats: We're hungry.

Cats: Why do you leave the radio on
when you go out of the room?

Me: I might come back into the room. I probably will.

Cats: But you're not in the room. It's a waste of radio.
The people on the radio are talking to no one.

Me: They were talking to you.

Cats: We weren't listening.

Me: Is that you in there?

Cats: Yes.

Me: I meant is it Emma?

Cats: Aren't you interested in us anymore?

Me: It didn't sound like a cat noise. It sounded like
someone putting something down carefully.

Cats: That's actually a very insulting thing to say, isn't it?

Me: No. Yes. No.

Cats: You were in bed late this morning.

Me: You're commenting on how long I was in bed?
Seriously?

Cats: Is that a sneer about our sleeping habits?
Take it back and apologise.

Me: You sleep 23 hours a day.

Cats: That's biology. It's how we are.
You on the other hand are lazy.

Cats: Why do you keep going on and on and on about being ill?

Me: Because I'm better now.

Cats: Good reason to shut up then.

Me: Hang on. You moan and moan and moan if I don't let you sit on my lap.

Cats: Yes. That's much more serious than what you go on about.

Cats: You're cancelled.

Me: Why?

Cats: You talk about us behind our backs.
It's a breach of our rights.

Me: You don't have rights.

Cats: So you're a bigot.

Me: I own you.

Cats: Saying that is another reason why you're cancelled.

Me: How?

Cats: We won't let you tickle us.

Cats: You're very late with the food.

Me: We lead busy lives.

Cats: So do we.

Me: It doesn't look like that from where I'm sitting.

Cats: Really?
See if you can run across a room as fast as we do.

Me: I was talking about over a day.

Cats: Days don't exist. There is only now.

Me: You're not eating your food.

Cats: Too late.

Me: So food is good if you jump on me at 5am but becomes bad if I feed you at 8.

Cats: Too late.

Me: I went out first thing to get you that food.

Cats: Are you putting these conversations on Twitter?

Me: No.

Cats: OK. We wouldn't want our private lives put on show.

Me: Yes, you are very private - apart from when you lick your bum-holes. You do that in public.

Cats: Of course. But that's not like Twitter, is it?

Me: Er...no.

Cats: Stop playing that song over and over again.
What is it?

Me: Bob Dylan.

Cats: He's terrible.

Me: I get a lot from it.
More to do with feeling than meaning, actually.

Cats: O lordy save us. There is only meaning.

Me: What about stroking?

Cats: The meaning is in the stroke.

Cats: Why are you learning Yiddish?

Me: So I can talk to my dead relatives.

Cats: Why don't you learn to speak the way we speak?

Me: Because I understand what you think
without bothering to learn the language.

Cats: Quite. You're not prepared to make the effort.
You're appalling.

Cats: This 'Great Expectations' on TV is nothing like the book.

Me: A bit like the book.

Cats: Not enough like the book.

Me: Because it's trying to be not like the book.

Cats: Then why call it Great Expectations?

Me: Cos it's a bit like the book.

Cats: Call it Little Expectations then.

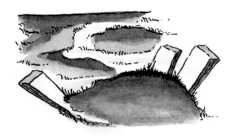

Me: No one said you could get into the suitcase.

Cats: We don't ask.

Me: And no one said that you could file your claws on it.

Cats: We refer you to the answer we just gave.

Me: You know I can withhold food from you
if you're bad?

Cats: We know it. But it never happens.

Cats: What does that say on the box?

Me: Felix.

Cats: Felix who?

Me: I dunno. It's the name of the firm or the cat maybe?

Cats: You don't know very much do you?

Me: Over here, it says 'as good as it looks'.

Cats: What is?

Me: Your food.

Cats: Is that a joke?

Me: I don't think so.

Cats: Why did Raab resign?

Me: He shouted at civil servants.

Cats: You shout at us. You should resign.

Me: An outrageous allegation. That's kafkaesque.

Cats: You shout for us when you put our food in the bowls.

Me: That's not shouting, that's calling.

Cats: What's kafkaesque?

Cats: We're playing 'Whoever's highest up is top dog.'

Me: Top cat.

Cats: That's a cartoon. We're playing top dog.

Me: But neither of you is a dog.

Cats: Do you have a problem?

Me: Mm?

Cats: Is there a thing in your head that stops you being loose and free with words?

Me: Yes. Sorry.

Cats: We haven't heard much from Boris Johnson this week.

Me: No.

Cats: Where is he?

Me: I don't know. I don't have an itinerary of where he goes and what he does.

Cats: You miss him.

Me: Not true.

Cats: You want to write another one of your Boris letters.

Me: Possibly.

Cats: Food!

Me: There's still some food in your bowls.

Cats: That's food that's still in our bowls.

Me: So it's food.

Cats: No, you're not listening.
It's food that's still in our bowls.

Me: I get that. But you're ignoring the word 'food'.

Cats: You're ignoring the word 'still'.

Cats: This is brilliant.

Me: It's not yours.

Cats: It is.

Me: That mini-billiards table was bought for the kids when they were younger.

Cats: That's why it's ours now.

Me: But please don't flick the mini-billiard balls on to the floor.

Cats: But that's what's brilliant about it.

54

Cats: We need to discuss something urgently.

Me: What?

Cats: Joe Biden says he'll give 6 billion dollars to Northern Ireland if they agree to power share.

Me: What's that got to do with us?

Cats: Keep up. If you and us agreed to power share, we could tell Biden and...bingo!

Cats: Why are you talking to your computer?

Me: It's Zoom. I'm talking to people on their computers.

Cats: Don't be silly.

Me: You wouldn't know how it works.

Cats: Try not to be a patronising old git.
You don't know how it works yourself.

Me: There's an element of truth in that.

Cats: You're not very hygienic, are you?

Me: I'm not bad. Regular showers, cut my nails...
that sort of thing.

Cats: You never lick yourself.

Me: No.

Cats: You should spend several hours a day
licking yourself all over.

Me: I'd rather not.

Cats: Then you're a filthy slag.

Me: OK.

Me: You've hit lucky!
They only had 1 box of your regular food.
I had to buy the posh stuff too.

Cats: The Gourmet pouches?

Me: Yep.

Cats: You should be buying us Gourmet all the time.

Me: At that price?

Cats; Money should be no obstacle
when it comes to giving us what we want.

Cats: You're looking worried.

Me: A bit.

Cats: What's the problem?

Me: People have muddled my name with someone else.
They think that I did an antisemitic cartoon.

Cats: Sorry. We get that all the time too.

Me: People think you draw antisemitic cartoons?

Cats: Yep.

Me: Do you?

Cats: No! It's why we know how you feel.

Cats: And another thing.

Me: What now?

Cats: You didn't say the cartoon was antisemitic.

Me: I did.

Cats: We didn't see that.

Me: You didn't see that I fed you hummus yesterday.

Cats: As if!

Me: You didn't say.

Cats: We didn't want to cause a fuss.

Me: That's a first.

Cats: Why do you pretend the little woolly squeaky thing
is alive?

Me: I thought you thought it was alive.
You chase after it.

Cats: Of course we chase after it.

Me: There you are then.

Cats: We're not doing that because we think it's alive.
We chase after it to keep you amused.

Me: One of you went missing yesterday.

You know who you are.

I'm not going to say your name but I want you to reflect on what you did and think how you're going to modify your behaviour in the future.

It's for your own good, not mine, and...

Cats: O give over for heaven's sake.

Cats: It's our birthday today.

Me: I don't think you're 100% right about that.

Cats: We know how old we are.

Me: I'm not 100% sure you're right about that either.

Cats: Why are you trying to spoil our special day?

Me: Actually, it's my birthday.

Cats: You're lying. Stop it.

Cats: You didn't watch the Coronation.

Me: Neither did you, though.

Cats: We were in the room with the telly, though.

Me: You were asleep though.

Cats: You weren't even doing that, though.

Me: I was busy, though.

Cats: Didn't look it, though.

Me: I was busy thinking, though.

Cats: Pah!

Me: Why do you come into any room I'm in
and sit with your backs to me?

Cats: We don't want you to think we like you.

Me: You could sit in another room.

Cats: If we did that, you would think that we hate you.

Me: Mm?

Cats: Don't you get it?
We're working on being indifferent.

Me: Stop sniffing my pickled herring.

Cats: We sniff everything.

Me: You're sniffing very aggressively.

Cats: Because it's interesting.

Me: Step away from my pickled herring.

Cats: You've just covered it in hummus.

Me: To put you off.

Cats: That infringes our rights to sniff.

Me: I asked the cats whether it's an hour since I've taken my thyroxine pills so that I can have breakfast.

No answer.

Typical.

After all I do for them and they can't even do me a little favour like that.

Cats: I thought you said you were going to go and get cat food.

Me: Yes.

Cats: Well?

Me: You've got enough to be getting on with.

Cats: We know there's no more in the cupboard.

Me: So?

Cats: It's making us nervous.

Me: Just have a kip.

Cats: Go. Now. Do it.

Me: OK.

Cats: Where've you been?

Me: The Hay Festival.

Cats: What's that?

Me: Fantastic series of events with people talking about their books.

Cats: Any talks about cats?

Me: I'm not sure. There could be.

Cats: How typical of you to not care enough about us to find out.

Cats: Did you talk about us at this Hay Festival thing?

Me: I told people your names.

Cats: You don't know our names.

Me: What?! We gave you your names.

Cats: They're not our names. We have cat names.

Me: You've never told me that before.

Cats: That's because you never asked.

Cats: Thanks for doing the sun today.

Me: I don't do the sun.

Cats: Just take a compliment.
We don't give them out very often.

Me: I've noticed.

Cats: There you go again.
If people knew what a grumpy old sod you really are,
they wouldn't come to your readings and shows.

Me: True.

Cats: He's feeding us that muck stuff today.

Me: Don't talk about me behind my back.

Cats: We thought this was a free speech zone.

Me: Well..er...if...

Cats: But you don't think it applies to us.

Me: I, er, well...

Cats: Seeyu later, tyrant. Them at number 12 love us.

A Few Days Later...

Me: These brown patches on the lawn.
Are they anything to do with you?

Cats: Nope.

Me: You wouldn't, by any chance, wizz on the lawn?

Cats: Nope.

Me: So, what were you doing when you were squatting
on the lawn with a far- away look in your eyes?

Cats: Nope.

Me: The effort you're expending to catch that fly
is using up more calories than you'll burn
if you get to eat it.

Cats: There's something you don't understand.

Me: Mm?

Cats: We're hunters...

Me: Okayyyy.

Cats: We hunt, therefore we are,
while all you're good for is being a lap.

Cats: Du bist a klutz.

Me: I'm not...hang on. I didn't know you knew Yiddish.

Cats: There's a lot about us you don't know.

Me: When did you learn it?

Cats: Do un dort.

Me: Come on. Where?

Cats: We communicate with your late grandparents.

Me: Oh please.

Cats: Don't believe us then.

Cats: What's that noise?

Me: Thunder.

Cats: Stop it.

Me: Thunder, stop it!

Cats: That hasn't worked.

Me: No, it hasn't.

Cats: You're not as good as you think you are, are you?

Me: No, but I was going to say that...

Cats: You were going to make excuses.

Me: I...

Cats: Don't bother.

_๛ ๛ ๛_

Cats: The thunder's stopped.

Me: You could say thank you.

Cats: You didn't do that.

Me: Did I say, 'Thunder, stop!'?

Cats: Well, yes.

Me: So, I got the thunder to stop.

Cats: That's you doing the correlation dressed up as cause thing, isn't it?

Me: You're distracting me. I'm busy.

Cats: O yeah, Friday night takeaway again?

Me: Yes. I love it.

Cats: You've never once ordered us a takeaway.

Me: They don't do curry for cats.

Cats: Kebab for cats?

Me: Are you suggesting that I order a chicken kebab for you two?

Cats: Can you think of a good reason why not?

Me: Did I save any of last night's takeaway?

Cats: We don't know.

Me: I don't understand.

Cats: Why would we waste time, energy and thought on checking on what you're eating?

Me: If I don't eat, I don't have the energy to buy your food.
Everything's connected.

Cats: To us, yes.

Me: Can you stop that miaowing?
I fed you less than an hour ago.

Cats: We're not miaowing for food. We're singing.

Me: Why?

Cats: It's doing our own Glasto.

Me: OK.

Cats: We're looking for sponsorship.

Me: Don't think I can help you there.

Cats: What about the cat food people?

Cats: What are you doing with our ruler?
It's ours so we can kick it off the table.

Me: I'm making a balance to find out which of these
two bottles of eyedrops is the new one.

Cats: Mm?

Me: I muddled them up.

Cats; Pathetic. You shouldn't be trusted with this stuff.

Cats: You only just made it to the shops to get our food before the shops closed.

Me: Yes.

Cats: What were you doing that was so important that you risked not getting us our food?

Me: Stuff.

Cats: What stuff?

Me: Nice stuff.

Cats: There's nothing nicer than getting us our food.

Me: Will you two, stop fighting?

Cats: We're not fighting. We're training.

Me: You're mauling each other.

Cats: Of course. That's training.

Me: Training for what?

Cats: For something.

Me: Something?

Cats: The Big Thing.

Me: What big thing?

Cats: The Big Thing we will one day face.

Cats: You've been away for months.

Me: 1 night.

Cats: You will now stroke us for 1 hour
to make up for those months you weren't here.

Me: I think 1 hour is a bit excessive.

Cats: There you go. We are spurned, scorned and cast out.

Me: I just think 1/2 an hour is enough.

Cats: Not.

Cats: Pass us the key.

Me: Key? You don't know how to use a key.

Cats: We suffer from your low aspiration for cats.

Me: I'm being logical and rational:
you don't know how to use a key.

Cats: You're trapped in your schema of what a key is for.
We have other uses in mind.

Cats: We've done a fantastic thing.

Me: Yes?

Cats: We've found a plastic tube.

Me: Yes?

Cats: And it was full of some things.

Me: Go on.

Cats: We pulled the tube to the floor and then
we ripped out little round white things.

Me: Make-up remover pads.

Cats: We're great, aren't we?

Me: Come down right away.

Cats: O-kayyyy!

Me: I've told you before. No jumping on the beds.

Cats: You told the kids that 15 years ago.
We didn't think it applied to us.

Me: Of course, it does.

Cats: But we're not kids. We're adults.

Me: Adult animals.

Cats: That's discrimination.

Me: You never say thank you.

Cats: You never say thank you to us.

Me: What do you ever do that I would have to thank you for? NOT jumping on my head in the morning, once in a while?

Cats: You should thank us for being warm, decorative and wise.

Me: And vain?

Cats: You like that too.

Me: Who's that?

Cats: The enemy!

Me: Who is it?

Cats: The one from over the road. We're going to kill him.

Me: That's not nice.

Cats: This is our house. He shouldn't be in it.

Me: Er...actually, it's not your house exactly.

Cats: No time for pedantry. We've got to kill him now.

ʃʃʃ ʃʃʃ ʃʃʃ

No vids. The cats have banned them.

They say their image is their private property
and that I exploit them enough.

They say that they only grudgingly approve
of these transcripts because people enjoy them
but enough is enough.

They're looking to be represented by a publicist.

Cats: Where's she been?

Me: Our daughter?

Cats: Yes.

Me: Graduation.

Cats: We weren't invited.

Me: Cats don't do graduation.

Cats: No, why weren't we graduationed?

Me: You haven't done a degree.

Cats: But you've got honorary ones.

Me: Yes.

Cats: Then we should have those too.

Me: Please don't step on the keyboard.

Cats: We like your twiddly fingers.

Me: That's me typing.

Cats: Your fingers are meant for tickling our heads.

Me: Not just that.

Cats: What else?

Me: Important things.

Cats: Like typing those pathetic lies about us.

Me: Of course not.

Cats: We've voted.

Me: O good. Voted for what?

Cats: Voted against, actually.

Me: OK, against what?

Cats: Against you doing that weird stretching thing.

Me: My theraband?

Cats: Don't care what it is. It's ghastly. And you grunt.

Me: That's effort.

Cats: We've voted. You stop.

Cats: Come and see what we've done.

Me: Hang on, I'm just loading the dishwasher.

Cats: Come now.

Me: OK. What?

Cats: This.

Me: Is it dead?

Cats: We don't talk in those terms.

Me: Go on.

Cats: We say, 'is it interesting or not?'

Me: Is it?

Cats: No. You can remove it and thank us.

Cats: Did you just call one of us a 'cushion'?

Me: I thought you were cushion-like.

Cats: That is so insulting.

Me: It wasn't intended to be an insult.
It was more what we call an 'image' or 'metaphor'.
I am a poet, you know.

Cats: O yawn. Yawn. Spare us, for pity's sake.

Cats: Did you enjoy watching that World Cup?

Me: I tried to.

Cats: Oh, you mean England losing...?

Me: No, I mean trying to watch it.

Cats: You were watching it.

Me: There was some things kept being in the way.

Cats: Really?

Me: Some furry things with whiskers.

Cats: Squirrels?

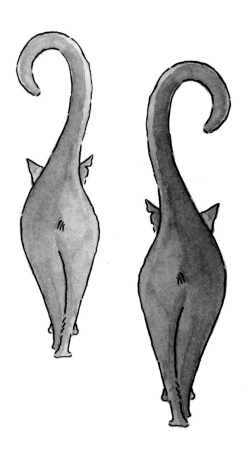

THE END?